MEN & BIKES

A COLOURING BOOK ANTIDOTE TO OBSESSIVE CYCLING DISORDER

FOR THOSE DAYS WHEN HE CAN'T GET OUT ON HIS BIKE

MEN & BIKES COLOURING BOOK
A COLOURING BOOK ANTIDOTE TO OBSESSIVE CYCLING DISORDER...
FOR THOSE DAYS WHEN HE CAN'T GET OUT ON HIS BIKE

ISBN: 978-1-913467-23-4

DISCLAIMER

MEN AND THEIR BIKES… LET'S FACE IT, THERE'S
NO COMPETING - BIKES COME FIRST. THEY'RE
TOP OF THE LIST FOR THE WEEKEND AND THE
MAIN TOPIC OF CONVERSATION THE REST OF
TIME.

IF THIS IS YOU, OR YOU KNOW SOMEONE
WHO WORSHIPS THEIR BIKE, THEN THIS BOOK
IS THE PERFECT ANTIDOTE TO OBSESSIVE
CYCLING DISORDER.

APPROXIMATELY 100 MILLION NEW BIKES
ARE MANUFACTURED EACH YEAR.

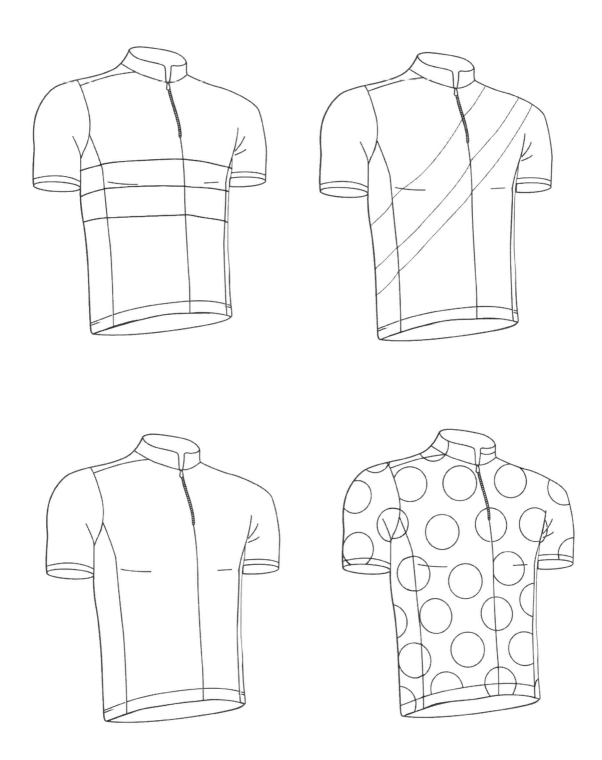

THERE ARE TWICE AS MANY BIKES IN THE
WORLD AS THERE ARE CARS.

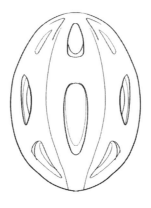

THE BICYCLE WAS ORIGINALLY INVENTED
IN FRANCE BUT THE MODERN DESIGN WE
RECOGNISE WAS CONCEIVED IN ENGLAND.

THE FASTEST SLIPSTREAM BIKE SPEED
RECORD WAS SET IN 2019 BY NEIL
CAMPBELL IN YORKSHIRE, WHO TRAVELLED
AT 280.571 KM/H (174.339 MPH).

40% OF ALL AMSTERDAM COMMUTES ARE
MADE BY BIKE.

THE MOST EXPENSIVE BIKE IN THE WORLD IS
A CUSTOMISED TREK MADONE WHICH WAS
DESIGNED BY DAMIEN HURST. IT SOLD FOR
£400,000 AT AUCTION.

EACH RIDER COMPETING IN THE TOUR DE FRANCE AIMS TO CONSUME 5000-7000 CALORIES A DAY TO KEEP THEMSELVES FUELLED.

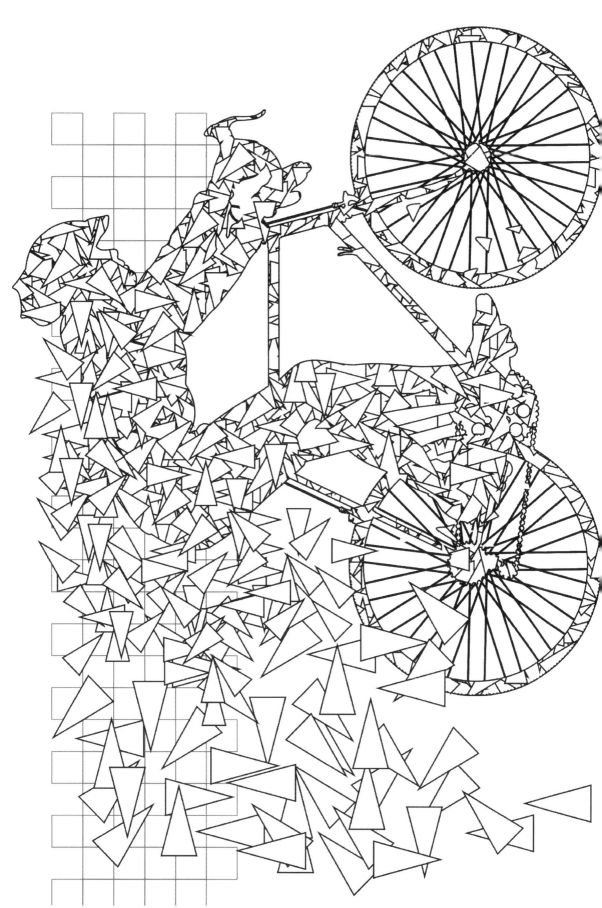

CYCLISTS SHAVE THEIR LEGS, NOT JUST BECAUSE OF AERODYNAMICS, BUT BECAUSE IT MAKES CLEANING INJURIES EASIER AND IS BETTER FOR SPORTS MASSAGE.

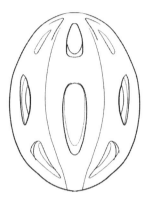

THE WORLD'S FIRST AIR-FILLED TYRE WAS
DEVELOPED FOR BICYCLES IN THE LATE
1880S AND WASN'T ADOPTED BY THE CAR
INDUSTRY UNTIL ALMOST A DECADE LATER.

THE TOUR DE FRANCE IS THE OLDEST STAGE RACE IN THE WORLD. FIRST HELD IN 1903, IT LASTS 21 DAYS AND COVERS OVER 3000KM.

THE WORLD'S LONGEST-RUNNING BIKE RACE
IS THE CATFORD CC HILL CLIMB IN THE UK,
WHICH FIRST BEGAN IN 1887 AND CONTINUES
UP TO THE PRESENT DAY.

THE LIGHTEST FULL RACING BIKE EVER
CONSTRUCTED WEIGHS LESS THAN 4KG.

MARK BEAUMONT HOLDS THE GUINNESS
WORLD RECORDS TITLE FOR THE FASTEST
CIRCUMNAVIGATION BY BIKE, WITH A TIME
OF 78 DAYS, 14 HOURS AND 40 MINUTES.

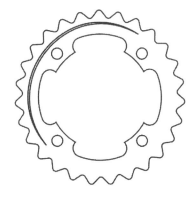

HARDKNOTT PASS IN CUMBRIA, ENGLAND,
IS CONSIDERED TO BE ONE OF THE UK'S
HARDEST CLIMBS WITH 30% GRADIENTS,
POOR SURFACES AND EPIC SCENERY.

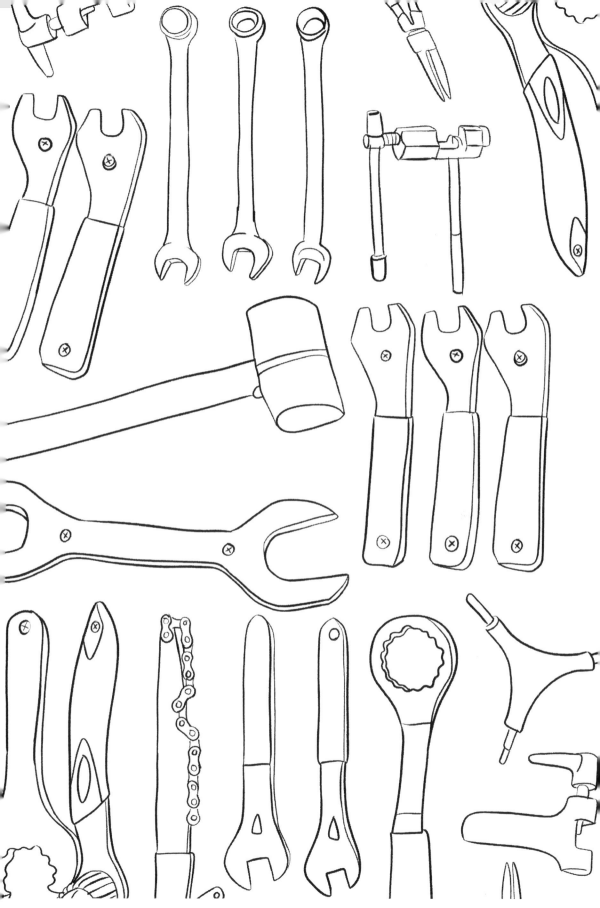

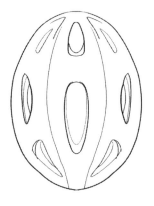

IN UK CYCLING, THE HOLY GRAIL OF HILLS IS BEALACH-NA-BA, APPLECROSS, IN THE SCOTTISH HIGHLANDS. IT'S CONSIDERED BY MANY TO BE THE TOUGHEST AND WILDEST ROAD CLIMB IN THE COUNTRY.

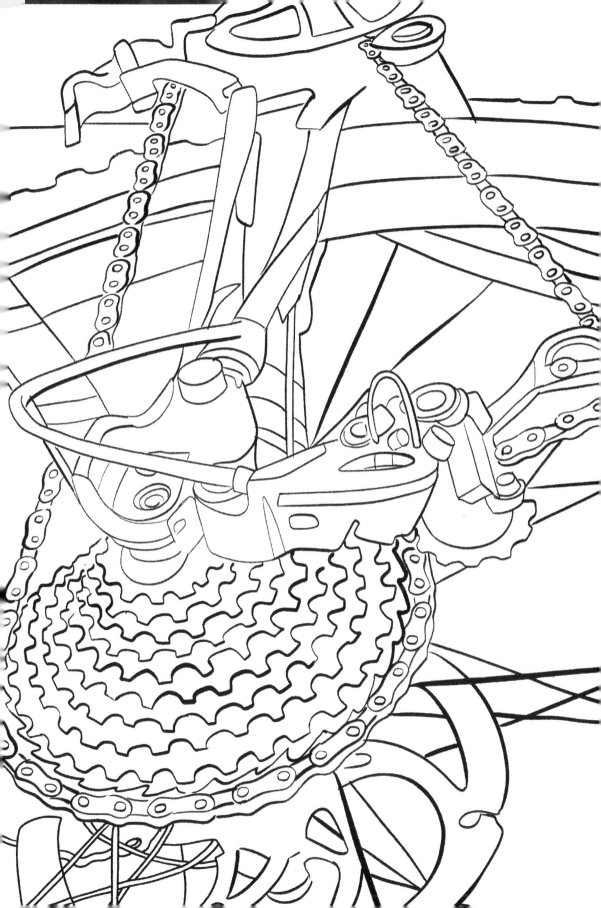

THE OFFICIAL RECORD FOR CYCLING LAND'S END TO JOHN O' GROATS IS 43 HOURS, 25 MINUTES AND 13 SECONDS.

105-YEAR-OLD ROBERT MARCHAND CYCLED 14 MILES IN 60 MINUTES, SETTING A DISTANCE RECORD IN THE 105-AND-ABOVE CATEGORY.

THE MOST ATTEMPTED STRAVA SEGMENT IN THE WORLD IS PRAÇA DA REITORIA, A FLAT HALF-KILOMETER LOOP IN SAO PAULO, BRAZIL.

ONE OF THE MOST POPULAR AND ICONIC SPORTIVES IN THE UK IS THE PRUDENTIAL RIDE LONDON-SURREY WHICH SEES 25,000 RIDERS CYCLE 100 MILES FROM SURREY, TO END WITH A SPRINT UP THE MALL IN LONDON.

THE TOUR DE FRANCE HAS HELD STAGES IN THE UK ON FOUR OCCASIONS OVER ITS HISTORY. THESE WERE 1974, 1994, 2007 AND MOST RECENTLY THE YORKSHIRE GRAND DEPART IN 2014.

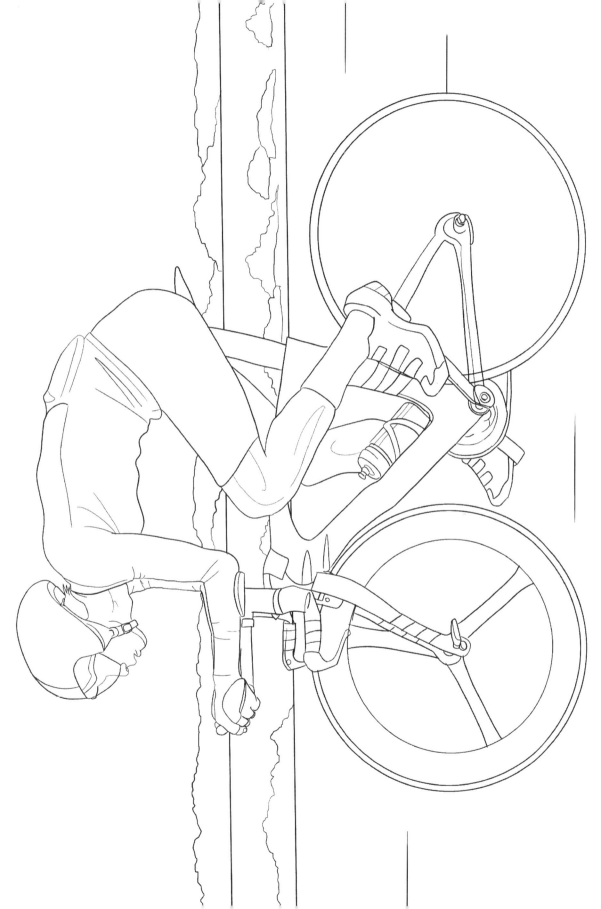

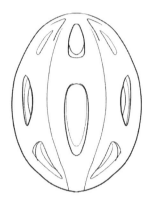

SIR CHRIS HOY IS THE SECOND MOST
DECORATED OLYMPIC CYCLIST OF ALL TIME,
HAVING WON A TOTAL OF SEVEN OLYMPIC
MEDALS; SIX GOLD AND ONE SILVER.

THE CURRENT WORLD RECORD FOR
DISTANCE TRAVELLED IN ONE HOUR ON A
BIKE IS 55.089KM (34.23 MILES).

ONLY FOUR RIDERS - JACQUES ANQUETIL, EDDY MERCKX, BERNARD HINAULT AND MIGUEL INDURAIN - HAVE WON THE TOUR DE FRANCE FIVE TIMES.

THE MAINTENANCE OF A BICYCLE IS 20
TIMES CHEAPER THAN A CAR.

CYCLING CAN IMPROVE BRAIN POWER. ACCORDING TO RESEARCH CARRIED OUT BY THE UNIVERSITY OF ILLINOIS, A 5% INCREASE IN CARDIO FITNESS FROM CYCLING CAN LEAD TO A 15% IMPROVEMENT IN MENTAL TESTS.

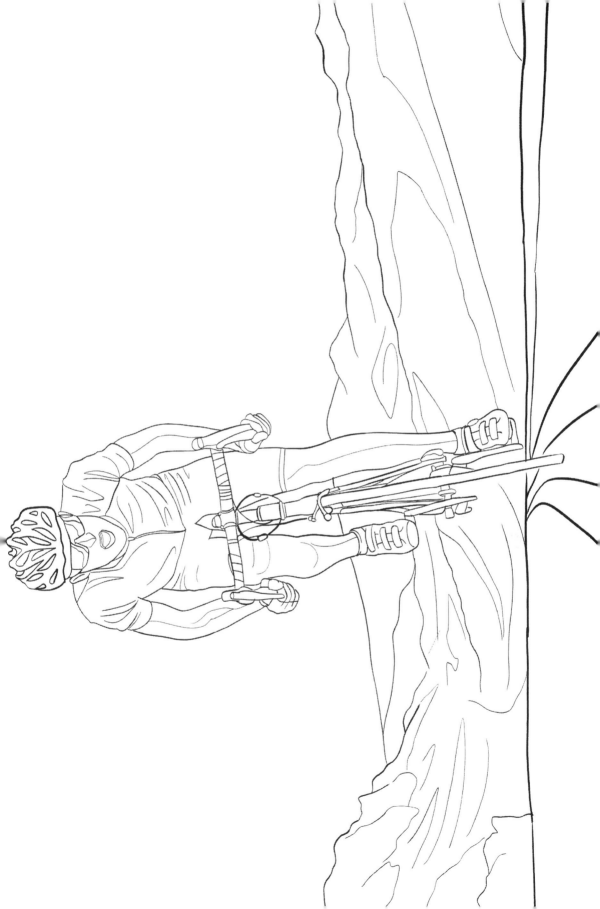

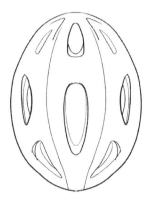

ACCORDING TO THE BRITISH HEART FOUNDATION, CYCLING 20 MILES A WEEK REDUCES THE RISK OF A HEART DISEASE TO 50% COMPARED TO THOSE WHO DO NOT EXERCISE.

AT A STEADY PACE OF CYCLING 15MPH,
YOU CAN BURN UP TO 600 CALORIES IN
AN HOUR, WHICH COULD BE OVER 4000
CALORIES IN A WEEK.

DRAFTING BEHIND ANOTHER RIDER TAKES ABOUT 30% LESS ENERGY THAN RIDING ALONE.

ENHANCED SLEEP: STUDIES AT STANFORD UNIVERSITY SCHOOL OF MEDICINE FOUND THAT CYCLING 30 MINUTES EVERY SECOND DAY IMPROVED THE SLEEP QUALITY OF INSOMNIA SUFFERERS, REDUCING THE TIME THEY TOOK TO FALL ASLEEP BY HALF AND INCREASED QUALITY SLEEP TIME BY 60 MINS.

'CYCLING BONK" IS A TERM USED TO
DESCRIBE WHEN YOUR BODY RUNS OUT
OF ENERGY DURING A RIDE - SIMILAR TO
'HITTING A WALL' IN OTHER SPORTS.

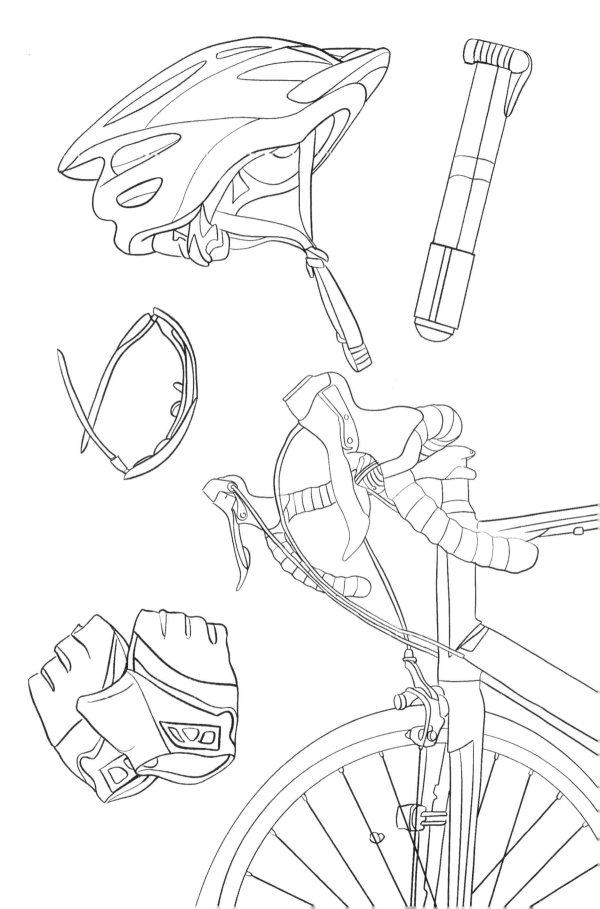

FOR LONG-DISTANCE RIDES, IT IS
RECOMMENDED TO REPLACE CARBS AT A
RATE OF 60-90G PER HOUR. STOCK UP ON
ENERGY BARS!

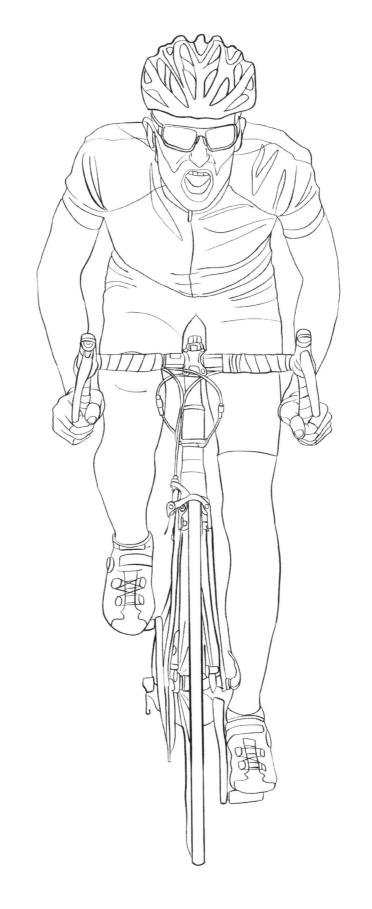

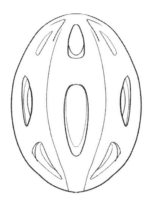

TO CALCULATE HOW MUCH WATER INTAKE YOU NEED FOR A LONG RIDE, WEIGH YOURSELF BEFORE YOUR RIDE AND THEN AGAIN AFTER YOU HAVE FINISHED. THE DIFFERENCE IN WEIGHT IS THE LEVEL OF FLUID THAT NEEDS REPLACING: 100G MEANS 100ML OF FLUID.

AN AVERAGE BIKE CHAIN CAN HAVE UP TO
116 LINKS HAVING MORE MOVING PARTS
THAN ANY OTHER BICYCLE COMPONENT.

RIDING IN THE MIDDLE OF A
WELL-ORGANISED PELOTON CAN REDUCE
DRAG DRAMATICALLY DOWN TO 5-10% OF
WHAT A SOLO RIDER WOULD ENDURE.

RAAM - RIDE ACROSS AMERICA BEGAN
IN 1982 AND IS ONE OF THE LONGEST
ANNUAL ENDURANCE EVENTS IN THE WORLD
COVERING 4800KM.

A CONDITION ASSOCIATED WITH EXTREME CYCLING DISTANCE IS 'SHERMER'S NECK'; WHEN YOUR NECK MUSCLES EFFECTIVELY 'GIVE UP' AND CAN'T HOLD YOUR HEAD UP DURING CYCLING.

STELVIO PASS IN THE ITALIAN ALPS BOASTS
SEVENTY HAIRPIN BENDS, WITH BRUTAL
CLIMBING OF 2,757 METRES, SO HIGH THAT
FOR MOST OF THE YEAR THE ROAD IS
BLOCKED BY SNOW AND ICE.

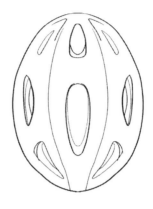

THE TRANSCONTINENTAL RACE IS AN
ULTRA-ENDURANCE, SELF-SUPPORTED,
SELF-NAVIGATED BIKE RACE ACROSS
EUROPE. IT'S GENERALLY 600KM LONGER
THAN THE TOUR DE FRANCE, WITH THE
WINNER USUALLY CROSSING THE LINE IN
APPROXIMATELY 10 DAYS, COMPARED TO
THE 21 DAYS THE TOUR TAKES.

I HAVE HEARD FOLKS SAY THAT THE BICYCLE IS GOING OUT OF FASHION. THAT IS SHEER NONSENSE! WHAT HAVE BOYS, OR STURDY YOUNG MEN, OR STURDY OLD ONES FOR THAT MATTER, TO DO WITH FASHION? THE BIKE IS HERE, AND IT HAS COME TO STAY, AND TO GO ON REVOLVING AS LONG AS FOLKS LIVE ON A REVOLVING WORLD.

- BOOK OF HEALTHFUL SPORTS FOR BOYS, PUBLISHED 1910

THE PATHWAY OF THE BIKER IS NOT ALWAYS
STRAIGHT AND SMOOTH, AS EVERY BOY
WHO HAS RIDDEN A WHEEL KNOWS.

- BOOK OF HEALTHFUL SPORTS FOR BOYS,
PUBLISHED 1910

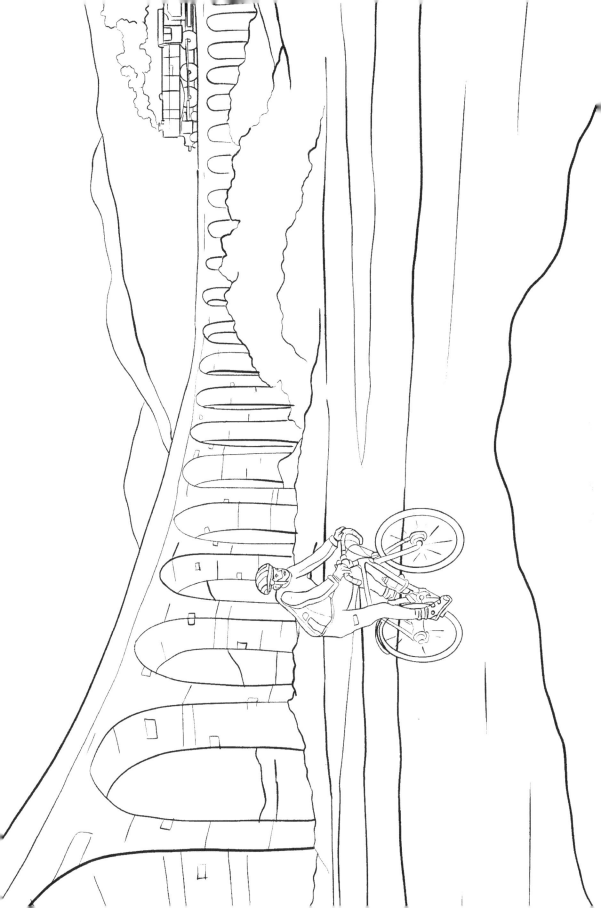

NO BOY IS WORTHY TO OWN A TOOL
OR A TOY, OR ANYTHING ELSE THAT IS
PERISHABLE, IF HE IS TOO LAZY OR TOO
CARELESS TO HAVE A PRIDE IN IT, AND
TO KEEP IT IN THE HIGHEST STATE OF
EFFICIENCY.

- BOOK OF HEALTHFUL SPORTS FOR BOYS,
PUBLISHED 1910

NO SADDLE IS PERFECT. THE PERFECT
SADDLE, AS THE PUBLIC LOOKS AT IT, IS
THE SADDLE THAT FITS EVERYBODY. IT
WILL NEVER BE MADE, FOR "PEOPLE ARE
DIFFERENT." THE TRUE WISDOM OF SADDLE
BUYING IS TO GET ONE THAT WILL FIT YOU.
CHOOSE A SADDLE AS YOU CHOOSE A PAIR
OF SHOES. WRONG SHOES CAUSE CORNS.
SO DO WRONG SADDLES. SADDLE CORNS
ARE DECIDEDLY UNCOMFORTABLE.

- THE MODERN BICYCLE AND ITS ACCESSORIES,
PUBLISHED 1898

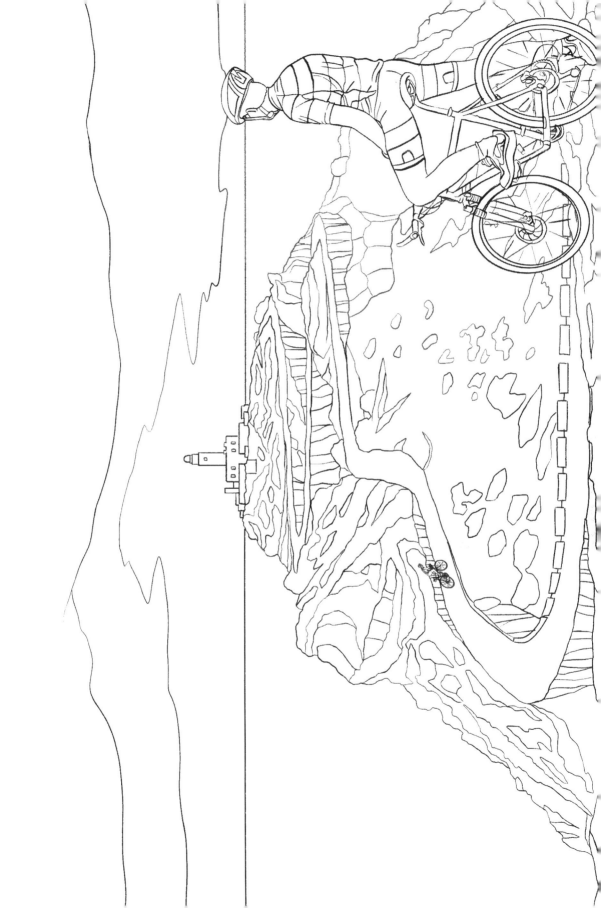

A VAGUE LONGING TO DO SOMETHING
FIRST FLATTERED, THEN IRRITATED, THEN
OPPRESSED ME. I HAD CONVINCED MYSELF
AGAINST MY WILL, AND WAS IN REALITY
STILL LONGING FOR THAT FORMLESS
SOMETHING.

- ACROSS A CONTINENT ON A BICYCLE,
PUBLISHED 1897

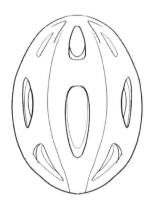

YES; THE JOURNEY WAS FORMIDABLE. IT
HAD NO ATTRACTIONS FOR ME IF IT WAS
OTHERWISE.

- ACROSS A CONTINENT ON A BICYCLE,
PUBLISHED 1897

YOU CAN FIT ABOUT 15 BICYCLES IN THE
SAME SPACE THAT ONE CAR OCCUPIES.

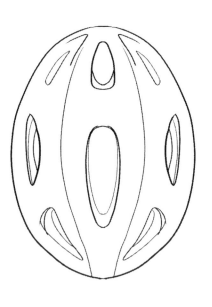

Printed in Great Britain
by Amazon

49802495R00054